MATHS
BOOSTER
Workbook

Scholastic Education, an imprint of Scholastic Ltd

Book End, Range Road, Witney, Oxfordshire, OX29 0YD

Registered office: Westfield Road, Southam, Warwickshire CV47 0RA

www.scholastic.co.uk

British Library Cataloguing-in-Publication Data

A catalogue record for this book is available from the British Library.

ISBN 978-1407-16087-0

Printed and bound by Ashford Colour Press

Author Paul Hollin

Editorial Rachel Morgan, Anna Hall, Mary Nathan, Marion Archer

Cover and Series Design Neil Salt and Nicolle Thomas

Layout Oxford Designers and Illustrators

Illustrations: Dave Smith @ Beehive Illustrations

Contents

How to use this book

This book will help you with what you need to know before you take the National Tests. You can complete Practice Test A first and use the grid to focus on specific topics you need more help on, or you can work through all of the activities in this book.

You can check the answers at **www.scholastic.co.uk/boosteranswers.**

The title of the topic.

What you should be able to do after you complete this page. You can tick off each one as you can do it.

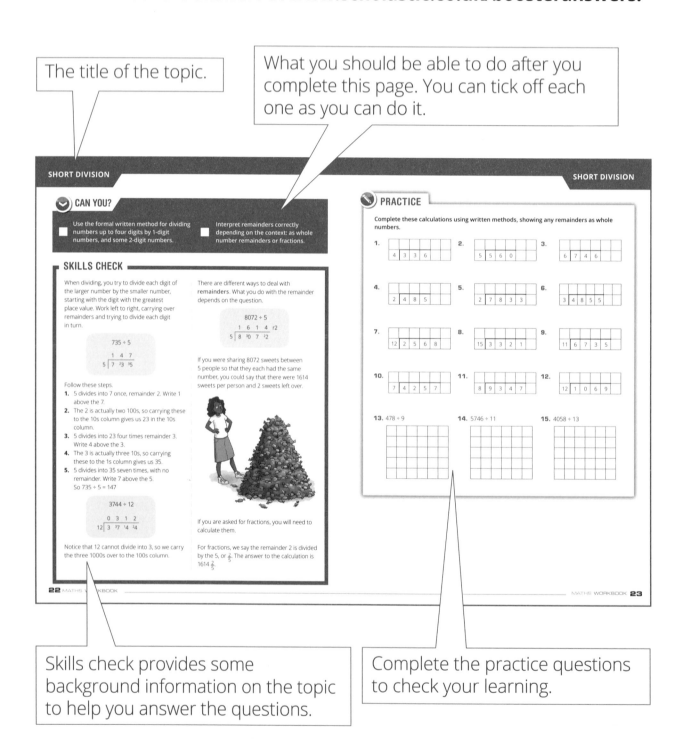

Skills check provides some background information on the topic to help you answer the questions.

Complete the practice questions to check your learning.

Progress chart

Topic	Revised	Practised	Achieved
Place value			
Negative numbers			
Factors and multiples			
Prime, square and cube numbers			
Mental methods			
Addition and subtraction			
Long multiplication			
Short division			
Long division			
Estimating and checking answers			
Understanding fractions			
Adding and subtracting fractions			
Multiplying and dividing fractions			
Decimals and money			
Fractions, decimals and percentages			
Ratio and proportion			
Scale factors			
Formulae and sequences			
Algebra: problems with one or two unknowns			
Measurement			
Perimeter, area and volume			
2D and 3D shapes			
Circles and angles			
Patterns and shapes			
Statistics			

CAN YOU?

- ☐ Read whole numbers up to ten million.
- ☐ Write whole numbers up to ten million.
- ☐ Round whole numbers up to ten million to the nearest power of 10.
- ☐ Order and compare whole numbers up to ten million.
- ☐ Read and write Roman numerals to 1000 (M).
- ☐ Recognise years written in Roman numerals.

SKILLS CHECK

Maths uses a **number system**. Our number system groups the digits in numbers into millions, thousands, hundreds, tens and ones – they have a **place value**. We can write numbers in words or in digits – remember to use commas and hyphens where needed.

| three million, | eight hundred and thirty-six thousand, | three hundred and fifty-two |

3,836,352

We can use place-value columns to help us read and write larger numbers.

Millions 1,000,000s	Hundred thousands 100,000s	Ten thousands 10,000s	Thousands 1000s	Hundreds 100s	Tens 10s	Ones 1s
3	8	3	6	3	5	2

We can use place value to compare numbers and to arrange them in order.

500 is bigger than 499, but smaller than 1000   In order: 499   500   1000

When deciding whether to **round up or down**, look at the digit to the right of the 10s, 100s or 1000s. If the digit is 5 or above we round up. If it is 4 or less, we round down.

35 rounds up to 40, but 34 rounds down to 30.

Look at these examples of rounding 9,347,506
9,347,500 to the nearest hundred
9,348,000 to the nearest thousand
9,350,000 to the nearest ten thousand
9,000,000 to the nearest million

Roman numerals

I = 1   II = 2   III = 3   IV = 4   V = 5   VI = 6   VII = 7   VIII = 8   IX = 9
X = 10   L = 50   C = 100   M = 1000

For the year 2019, we write MMXIX: 1000 (M) + 1000 (M) + 10 (X) + 9 (IX).

 **PRACTICE**

1. Write these numbers in numerals.

    a. seventy-five thousand, four hundred and three: _____

    b. five million, six hundred and twenty-one thousand, seven hundred: _____

2. Write these numbers in words.

    a. 62,000 _____

    b. 5,423,681 _____

    _____

3. Write these numbers in order, smallest to largest.

    43,085   305,221   842,365   786,289   947   80,001

    _____   _____   _____   _____   _____   _____

4. Identify the value of the underlined digit in each number. Write your answer in words.

    a. 4<u>3</u>5,210 _____   **b.** 23,<u>6</u>75 _____

    c. 8,<u>5</u>37,051 _____   **d.** <u>4</u>,433,624 _____

5. Round each number to the nearest:

    a. 10: 6017 _____   **b. 1000:** 6017 _____

    c. 100: 85,051 _____   **d. 10,000:** 8,423,681 _____

    e. million: 8,423,681 _____   **f. 100,000:** 283,500 _____

6. Write the Roman numerals in figures.

    a. XI _____   **b.** XXV _____   **c.** XIX _____

    d. CCC _____   **e.** LX _____   **f.** XCV _____

7. Draw lines to match each year to its equivalent in Roman numerals.

MMI	MCMXC	MCMXCIX	MMX	MM

1999	2010	2001	2000	1990

CAN YOU?

☐ Read number lines that go through zero.

☐ Count back and forwards across zero.

☐ Calculate intervals across zero.

☐ Use negative numbers in context, such as temperatures, bank accounts and sea level.

SKILLS CHECK

Numbers can be **negative** or **positive**. Count forwards from zero for positive numbers, and backwards from zero for negative numbers.

When you count across zero, remember to include it like any other number. For the number line below, we would say 3, 2, 1, 0, –1, –2.

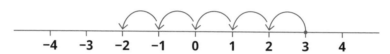

Gina and her friend record the temperature every 2 hours for a day.

Noon	2pm	4pm	6pm	8pm	10pm	Midnight	2am	4am	6am	8am	10am
5°C	6°C	5°C	3°C	3°C	1°C	–1°C	–2°C	–3°C	–2°C	0°C	4°C

How much did the temperature drop between noon and midnight?
Count down from +5 to –1. We count 6°C. Therefore, the temperature dropped 6°C.
(Notice that the answer is not negative.)

Look at the mountain in the picture. How far is it from the top to the very bottom of the mountain?
We simply add the amounts above and below sea level:
500 + 35 = 535m

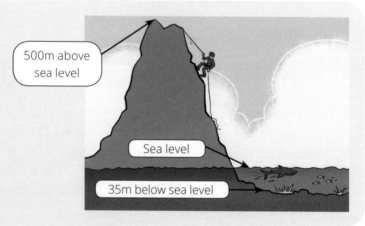

500m above sea level

Sea level

35m below sea level

The graph shows how the amount of money in a bank account changes over a year. The account started in credit but ended up overdrawn.
The difference between the start and end of the year is:
£300 + £250 = £550

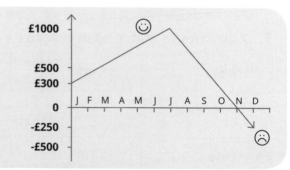

PRACTICE

1. Mark the temperatures on the thermometers.

   a. 3° −2° −4°

   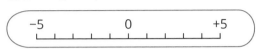

   b. −12° −2° −9°

   −15   0

2. Write the missing numbers in these sequences.

   a.

   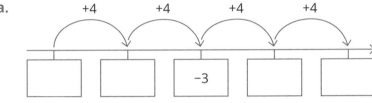

   b.

   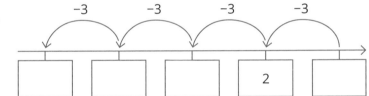

3. A gardener sets a digital thermometer to record the highest and lowest temperatures in a garden. The highest temperature was at 2pm and was 6°C. The lowest temperature was at 3am and was recorded as −5°C. Calculate how much the temperature changed between 2pm and 3am.

   _____

4. In winter, Moscow is 25°C colder than London. If the temperature in London is 7°C, what will it be in Moscow?

   _____

5. A man dives off a 5 metre diving board and touches the bottom of the swimming pool. If the pool is 2.5 metres deep, how far has he travelled altogether?

   _____

6. On Tuesday, a student had £200 in her bank account. The next day she paid her rent, and her bank balance was −£175. How much was her rent?

   _____

CAN YOU?

☐ Explain what a factor and a multiple is.

☐ Find the highest common factor for two or more numbers.

☐ Find the lowest common multiple for two or more numbers.

SKILLS CHECK

Factors are whole numbers that divide exactly into numbers.

$5 \times 3 = 15$, so 5 and 3 are both factors of 15. They are called a factor pair.

Some numbers have lots of factors. The factors of 24 are 1, 2, 3, 4, 6, 8, 12, 24.
In their pairs, these are:

1×24 $\qquad$ 2×12 $\qquad$ 3×8 $\qquad$ 4×6

A **common factor** is a number that is a factor of two different numbers.

3 is a factor of 12 and of 15
6 and 30 have common factors of 1, 2, 3 and 6

A **multiple** is a number that can be divided exactly by another number.

$18 \div 3 = 6$, so 18 is a multiple of 3 and 6

You can see how multiples and factors are related: 5 is a factor of 15, so 15 is a multiple of 5.

A **common multiple** is a number that is a multiple of two different numbers. Think about factor pairs.

$3 \times 5 = 15$, so 15 is a common multiple of 3 and 5.

PRACTICE

1. **Complete the sentence below.**

   Every number with a factor of 15 must also have factors of _____, _____ and _____.

2. **Write the lowest common multiple for each pair of numbers.**

   a. 2 and 3: _____ **b.** 3 and 8: _____ **c.** 6 and 10: _____

3. **Write a multiple of 7 in each box.**

   a. $20 <$ ☐ < 30 **b.** $491 <$ ☐ < 500

CAN YOU?

☐ Explain what a prime number and a prime factor is.

☐ Use number skills to decide if a number is a prime or not.

☐ Recall and use square numbers and cube numbers.

☐ Use ^{2} for square numbers and ^{3} for cube numbers.

SKILLS CHECK

A **square number** is a number multiplied by itself.

$3^2 = 3 \times 3 = 9$

(Notice the small 2 we use to show this.)

A **cube number** is a number multiplied by itself, and then by itself again.

$4^3 = 4 \times 4 \times 4 = 64$

A **prime number** can only be divided exactly by itself and 1, but 1 is not a prime number.
An even number (except 2) is not a prime.
A number that ends in 0 or 5 can be divided by 5, so is not a prime.
A number whose digits add to a multiple of 3 can be divided by 3, so is not prime.

57: 5 + 7 = 12, so 57 is not a prime number

A **prime factor** is a prime number that is a factor of a number. Any number can be shown as the product of its prime factors.

60: 60 = 2 × 30   30 = 2 × 15   15 = 3 × 5
So, 60 = 2 × 2 × 3 × 5

PRACTICE

1. Write the numbers 1–10 in the sorting diagram below.

	Prime	Not prime
Even		
Odd		

2. Two prime numbers have the lowest common multiple of 55. What are the numbers?

   _____ and _____

3. Write all the prime numbers between 90 and 100. _____

4. **a.** $7^2 =$ _____   **b.** $2^2 + 3^2 =$ _____   **c.** $10^2 - 8^2 =$ _____

CAN YOU?

☐ Use your knowledge of number facts and mental methods to add and subtract larger numbers.

☐ Use your multiplication tables to multiply and divide rapidly, and use these facts to calculate with larger numbers.

☐ Use the correct order of operations to perform mental calculations involving mixed operations.

SKILLS CHECK

Mental methods help us solve calculations faster, but remember that in tests you get marks for showing your method for long multiplication and long division.

Before calculating, remember to work out whether a mental or written method would be most appropriate.

For 7998 + 3462, you can see that 7998 is only 2 less than 8000 so you could add 3462 to 8000 and then subtract 2.

$$8000 + 3462 = 11,462$$
$$11,462 - 2 = 11,460$$

Remember you can use what you know about partitioning when **adding and subtracting**:

$$231 + 310 = 200 + 300 + 31 + 10 = 541$$
$$458 - 230 = 458 - 200 - 30 = 228$$

Know your **multiplication** tables by heart, and remember that these give you **division** facts too.

$$3 \times 7 = 21, \text{ so } 7 \times 3 = 21$$
$$21 \div 7 = 3, \text{ and } 21 \div 3 = 7$$

Multiplying and dividing powers of 10 can sometimes be done using mental methods.

$$40 \times 7 = 280 \ (4 \times 7 = 28; 28 \times 10 = 280)$$
$$60 \times 50 = 3000 \ (6 \times 5 = 30; 30 \times 10 \times 10 = 3000)$$
$$3600 \div 9 = 400 \ (36 \div 9 = 4; 4 \times 100 = 400)$$
$$220 \div 20 = 11 \ (220 \div 10 = 22; 22 \div 2 = 11)$$

Remember: BIDMAS: This is the order in which you carry out operations in a calculation:
- **B**rackets
- **I**ndices ('Indices' is another word for 'powers', like ^{2} and ^{3})
- **D**ivision and **M**ultiplication (do together in the order they come, left to right)
- **A**ddition and **S**ubtraction (do together in the order they come, left to right).

$$15 \times 6 - 4^3 + 54 \div 6$$
$$= 15 \times 6 - 64 + 54 \div 6$$
$$= 90 - 64 + 9$$
$$= 35$$

This example involves brackets:
$$(36 - 27) \times 49 \div 7 - 8 + 3$$
$$= 9 \times 49 \div 7 - 8 + 3$$
$$= 63 - 8 + 3$$
$$= 58$$

PRACTICE

1. a. 45 + 19 = _____   **b.** 652 + 305 = _____   **c.** 2999 + 4525 = _____

   d. 95 + 462 = _____   **e.** 52 + 23 + 21 = _____   **f.** 9000 + 7000 = _____

2. a. 87 − 21 = _____   **b.** 463 − 96 = _____   **c.** 1000 − 105 = _____

   d. 265 − 112 = _____   **e.** 7625 − 4500 = _____   **f.** 84,000 − 11,000 = _____

3. a. 273 + 700 = _____   **b.** 6752 + 3300 = _____   **c.** 450 + 650 = _____

   d. 300 + 105 = _____   **e.** 550 + 199 = _____   **f.** 8300 + 1100 = _____

4. a. 563 − 200 = _____   **b.** 4852 − 3300 = _____   **c.** 7392 − 5000 = _____

   d. 245 − 90 = _____   **e.** 3000 − 2500 = _____   **f.** 600 − 398 = _____

5. a. 47 × 100 = _____   **b.** 8 × 300 = _____   **c.** 20,000 × 2 = _____

   d. 70 × 50 = _____   **e.** 300 × 30 = _____   **f.** 84 × 100 = _____

6. a. 23 × 3 = _____   **b.** 36 × 2 = _____   **c.** 4 × 5 × 6 = _____

   d. 125 × 2 = _____   **e.** 310 × 3 = _____   **f.** 7 × 8 × 10 = _____

7. a. 8430 ÷ 10 = _____   **b.** 160 ÷ 4 = _____   **c.** 300 ÷ 30 = _____

   d. 50,000 ÷ 2 = _____   **e.** 2100 ÷ 7 = _____   **f.** 2100 ÷ 70 = _____

8. a. 30 − 5 × 4 = _____   **b.** 45 ÷ 9 − 4 = _____

   c. 4 × 6 ÷ (3 + 5) = _____   **d.** 4 + 3 × 6 − 8 = _____

   e. (10 × 5 − 20) ÷ 6 = _____   **f.** $3 \times (2 + 6) - 4^2$ = _____

CAN YOU?

- [ ] Use the formal written methods to add and subtract larger numbers.

- [ ] Use your understanding of how the formal written methods work to solve problems involving missing digits in calculations.

- [ ] Solve real-life problems by using the formal written methods.

- [ ] Use inverse calculations to check your answers.

SKILLS CHECK

To add and subtract larger numbers, use a written method. Lay out your work neatly, arranging the numbers in their place value columns.

You can add numbers in any order. You may find it easier to arrange them in order of largest to smallest. **Remember** to carry any numbers across at the bottom.

24 + 553 + 489 + 890:

	8	9	0
	5	5	3
	4	8	9
+		2	4
1	9	5	6
		₂	₁

Remember to exchange numbers if you need to in subtractions.

11640 − 4284:

	₁Ⅺ	¹1	⁵6̶	¹³4̶	¹0
−		4	2	8	4
		7	3	5	6

6205 − 3327:

	⁵6̶	¹¹2̶	⁹0̶	¹5
−	3	3	2	7
	2	8	7	8

Remember, subtraction is the *inverse* of addition and addition is the inverse of subtraction. You can use an inverse calculation to check your work.

For questions with missing digits, start with the 1s column.

	3	☐	5
+	2	7	☐
	6	3	1

5 plus something gives 1 in the answer, so the missing digit must be 6 (5 + 6 = 11). We have to carry 1 to the 10s column.

Looking at the 10s column, something plus 7 plus 1 = 3, so the missing 10s digit must be 5 (7 + 1 + 5 = 13). We have to carry 1 to the 100s column.

As a final check, adding the 100s gives: 3 + 2 + 1 = 6

For real-life problems, you need to select the correct operations and in the right order. Try to give yourself a rough estimate of the answer at the start so that you can see if your calculations make sense. (There are more multi-step problems in the measures section.)

PRACTICE

Complete these calculations using written methods.

1.

		4	6	7
	+	2	2	5

2.

	2	3	0	7
+	1	8	9	5

3.

	5	3	8	4	9	3
+	4	8	1	3	5	5

4.

	2	3	6	2	8
	1	2	2	1	3
+		4	1	8	4

5. 5238 + 3471 + 2305

6. 1,829,304 + 1,222,417 + 425,320

7.

		3	7	5
	−	1	4	7

8.

		4	3	7	2
	−	1	5	4	7

9.

	2	3	6	0	3
−	1	7	3	3	5

10.

	4	3	2	7	1	5
−	2	4	1	5	1	7

11. 37,236 − 23,428

12. 4,305,624 − 1,473,466

13. Add one hundred and forty-five thousand, six hundred and twenty-one and three hundred and sixty-eight thousand, three hundred and eighty.

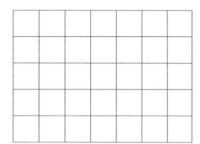

14. Subtract one hundred and forty-five thousand, six hundred and twenty-one from three hundred and sixty-eight thousand, three hundred and eighty.

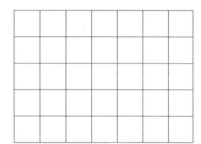

Insert the missing digits to complete the following calculations.

15.
```
    3 0 ☐
 +  1 ☐ 8
 ─────────
    4 6 3
```

16.
```
    4 ☐ 5
 −  2 3 8
 ─────────
  ☐ 6 7
```

17.
```
    3 ☐ 4 ☐
 +  ☐ 4 ☐ 2
 ───────────
    8 0 0 3
```

18.
```
    7 ☐ 4 6 5
 +  ☐ 3 2 8 ☐
 ─────────────
  ☐ 3 5 ☐ 4 6
```

19.
```
    2 3 ☐ 3 5
 −    7 5 ☐ 5
 ─────────────
    1 6 2 8 ☐
```

20.
```
    4 3 2 8 4 ☐
 −  3 0 ☐ 2 4 5
 ───────────────
    1 ☐ 5 5 9 5
```

Solve these problems. Show your method.

21. At a football match, 23,475 support the blue team and 19,850 support the red team. How many supporters are there in total?

22. A large city has a river running through it. 2,347,683 people live north of the river and 5,625,427 live south of the river. How many people in total live in the city?

23. Ibrar says

4,381,305 + 2,095,836 = 6,477,141

Ibrar is correct.
Explain how you know.

_____

_____

_____

CAN YOU?

- [ ] Use the formal written method to multiply larger numbers by 2-digit numbers.
- [ ] Use your understanding of how the formal written methods work to solve problems involving missing digits in calculations.
- [ ] Solve real-life problems by using the formal written methods.
- [ ] Use inverse calculations (division) to check your answers.

SKILLS CHECK

Look at this calculation: 15 × 375.

		3	7	5	
	×		1	5	
	1	8³	7²	5	← × **5**
	3	7	5	0	← × **10**
	5	6	2	5	
		1	1		

Remember: for a long multiplication, you can get a mark for showing your method, even if your answer is wrong.

For questions with missing digits only insert the answers when you are sure. Work through the calculation in the correct order for the method you have been taught. If you go step by step, you can use the clues to solve it.

To complete this long multiplication, follow these steps.

1. Arrange the two numbers in columns, with the larger number at the top.

2. Multiply the top number by the 1s digit of the lower number. Start with the 1s digit (5 × 5 = 25). Notice that the 2 is written in the 10s column. Then multiply the 10s (7 × 5 = 35 + 2 = 37), and write the 3 in the 100s column. Finally, multiply the 100s (3 × 5 = 15 + 3 = 18).

3. Multiply the top number by the 10s digit (the 10). Add a zero to the 1s column, and then just multiply by 1: 5 × 1 = 5 in the 10s column, then 7 × 1 = 7 in the 100s column, and 3 × 1 = 3 in the 1000s column.

4. Add the two numbers together.

				5	☐
		×	3	4	
		2	0	8	
	1	5	☐	0	
	1	7	6	8	

In this example, the first calculation is 4 × ☐. The answer is 8, so the missing digit could be 2. Yet it could also be 7 (since 4 × 7 = 28), with 2 carried forward. However, you can see that 4 × 5, the second calculation, made 20, so there was nothing carried forward. The first missing digit must be 2.

The second blank is now easy to complete (3 × 2 = 6), and the final line proves that this is correct.

PRACTICE

Complete these calculations using written methods.

1.

				3	2
			×	1	2

2.

				3	5
			×	2	3

3.

			1	3	5
		×		2	5

4.

			2	6	7
		×		4	3

5.

		1	4	2	3
	×			5	6

6.

		2	0	8	3
	×			2	7

7. 41 × 15

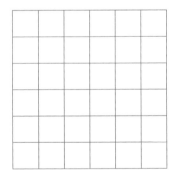

8. 29 × 15

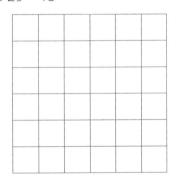

9. 207 × 32

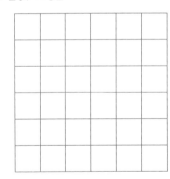

10. 356 × 34

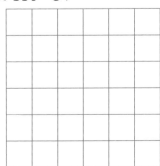

11. 2405 × 37

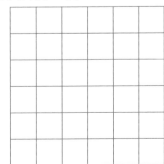

12. 4285 × 63

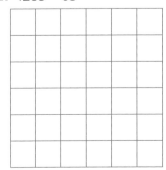

Insert the missing digits to complete these calculations.

13.

```
      ☐ 2
  ×   1 4
  ─────────
    1 2 8
    3 ☐ 0
  ─────────
    4 4 8
  ─────────
```

14.

```
          4 ☐
    ×     3 2
  ───────────
          ☐ 6
    1 2 9 0
  ───────────
    1 ☐ 7 6
  ───────────
```

15.

```
        5 4
  ×   ☐ 3
  ─────────
    1 ☐ 2
  1 6 2 0
  ─────────
  1 ☐ 8 ☐
  ─────────
```

16.

```
      ☐ 2 5
  ×     1 ☐
  ───────────
      5 0 0
    1 2 ☐ 0
  ───────────
    1 7 5 0
  ───────────
```

17.

```
      3 4 2
  ×     ☐ ☐
  ─────────────
      1 3 6 8
    1 3 6 8 0
  ─────────────
    1 5 0 4 8
  ─────────────
```

18.

```
      2 ☐ 0 3
  ×       1 ☐
  ───────────────
    1 2 5 1 5
    2 5 0 3 0
  ───────────────
    3 ☐ ☐ ☐ 5
  ───────────────
```

Solve these problems. Show your method.

19. Nails are sold in boxes of 2500. How many nails will there be in 25 boxes?

20. A football team manager promises all 11 players on the team that they will each receive a £625 bonus if they win. How much would this cost the manager altogether?

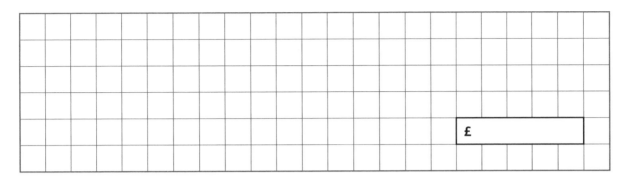

£

21. In a class of 28 children, each child completes 12 pieces of homework each term. How many pieces of homework will their teacher have to mark each term?

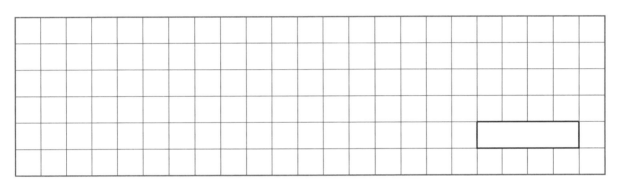

22. There are 24 hours in a day and 365 days in a year. How many hours are there in a year?

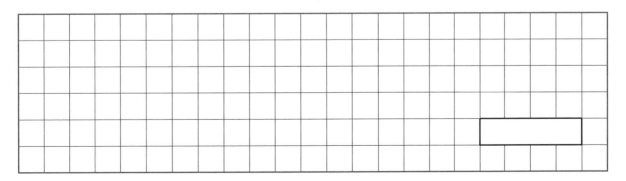

CAN YOU?

☐ Use the formal written method for dividing numbers up to four digits by 1-digit numbers, and some 2-digit numbers.

☐ Interpret remainders correctly depending on the context: as whole number remainders or fractions.

SKILLS CHECK

When dividing, you try to divide each digit of the larger number by the smaller number, starting with the digit with the greatest place value. Work left to right, carrying over remainders and trying to divide each digit in turn.

$$735 \div 5$$

$$\begin{array}{c} \quad 1 \quad 4 \quad 7 \\ 5 \overline{\smash{)}\, 7 \ ^2 3 \ ^3 5} \end{array}$$

Follow these steps.

1. 5 divides into 7 once, remainder 2. Write 1 above the 7.
2. The 2 is actually two 100s, so carrying these to the 10s column gives us 23 in the 10s column.
3. 5 divides into 23 four times remainder 3. Write 4 above the 3.
4. The 3 is actually three 10s, so carrying these to the 1s column gives us 35.
5. 5 divides into 35 seven times, with no remainder. Write 7 above the 5.
   So 735 ÷ 5 = 147

$$3744 \div 12$$

$$\begin{array}{c} \quad 0 \quad 3 \quad 1 \quad 2 \\ 12 \overline{\smash{)}\, 3 \ ^3 7 \ ^1 4 \ ^2 4} \end{array}$$

Notice that 12 cannot divide into 3, so we carry the three 1000s over to the 100s column.

There are different ways to deal with **remainders**. What you do with the remainder depends on the question.

$$8072 \div 5$$

$$\begin{array}{c} \quad 1 \quad 6 \quad 1 \quad 4 \quad r2 \\ 5 \overline{\smash{)}\, 8 \ ^3 0 \ 7 \ ^2 2} \end{array}$$

If you were sharing 8072 sweets between 5 people so that they each had the same number, you could say that there were 1614 sweets per person and 2 sweets left over.

If you are asked for fractions, you will need to calculate them.

For fractions, we say the remainder 2 is divided by the 5, or $\frac{2}{5}$. The answer to the calculation is $1614\frac{2}{5}$.

PRACTICE

Complete these calculations using written methods, showing any remainders as whole numbers.

1.

4	3	3	6		

2.

5	5	6	0		

3.

6	7	4	6		

4.

2	4	8	5	

5.

2	7	8	3	3	

6.

3	4	8	5	5	

7.

12	2	5	6	8	

8.

15	3	3	2	1

9.

11	6	7	3	5

10.

7	4	2	5	7	

11.

8	9	3	4	7

12.

12	1	0	6	9

13. 478 ÷ 9

14. 5746 ÷ 11

15. 4058 ÷ 13

 **CAN YOU?**

☐ Use the correct written method for dividing numbers up to four digits by 1- or 2-digit numbers.	☐ Interpret remainders correctly depending on the context: as whole number remainders, fractions or decimals.

SKILLS CHECK

Look at the calculation and follow these steps.

	0	2	2	4	r9	
15	3	3	6	9		
–	3	0				(2 × 15)
		3	6			
	–	3	0			(2 × 15)
			6	9		
		–	6	0		(4 × 15)
				9		

1. Lay out the numbers as shown.
2. Start with the digit that has the greatest place value.
3. 15 cannot divide into 3, so we carry 3 forward and divide 15 into 33.
4. Two 15s are 30, so that is the most we can divide.
5. We then calculate the remainder, saying 2 × 15 = 30, then 33 – 30 = 3.
6. We bring down the 6 to make 36.
7. 15 will divide into this 2 times; three 15s are 45, which is too many.
8. We then calculate the remainder, saying 2 × 15 = 30, then 36 – 30 = 6.
9. Bring the 9 down to give us the next number: 69.
10. We know that 15 goes into 60 four times, but not five. So, we subtract 60 (15 × 4) from 69, giving us a remainder of 9.

Remember: for a long division, you can get a mark for showing your method, even if your answer is wrong.

A group of 15 children swam a total of 3369 lengths. What was the average number of lengths the children swam?

3369 ÷ 15 = 224.6
The remainder becomes a decimal. Add .0 to the number you're dividing and then carry the remainder over. 90 ÷ 15 = 6.

There were 3369 cartons of juice. A box holds 15 cartons. How many boxes are needed for all the cartons?

We round up the remainder because we need all the cartons to be boxed.
We have 224 full boxes and we need one more for the 9 cartons left, that's 225 boxes in total.

15 children were making models from 3369 matchsticks. How many matchsticks did each child receive?

For this, we would express the remainders as a fraction: $\frac{9}{15}$ (or $\frac{3}{5}$ when simplified).
The answer is $224\frac{9}{15}$.

 PRACTICE

Complete these calculations using written methods, leaving remainders as whole numbers where necessary.

1.

12	3	7	2	

2.

15	3	3	0	

3.

13	1	5	7	3

4.

25	2	7	8	0
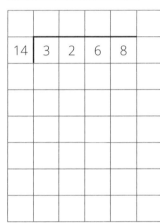

5.

14	3	2	6	8

6.

11	4	5	7	9

7. 450 ÷ 15

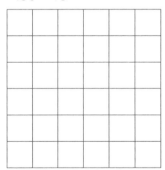

8. 693 ÷ 11

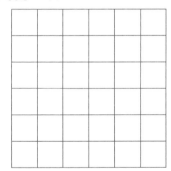

9. 1254 ÷ 12

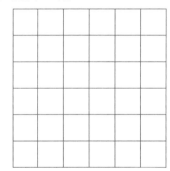

10. 2803 ÷ 25

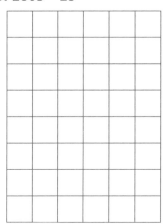

11. 333 ÷ 16

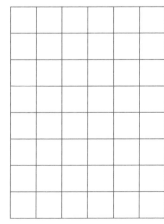

12. 6002 ÷ 12

Use long division to solve these word problems. Show your working out.

13. A jumbo box of popcorn has 1000 pieces in it. If 8 children share it equally, how many pieces will they each get?

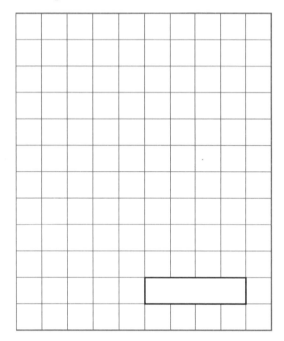

14. A football stadium is divided into 8 equal seating areas. If the total number of spectators is 48,400, how many people does each area hold?

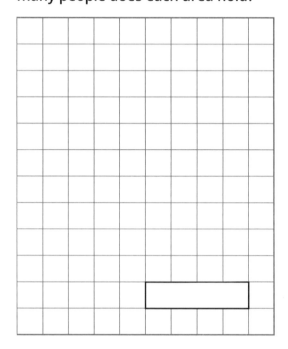

15. A class of 25 children raise £3275 in a sponsored cycle ride. What is the average amount raised per person?

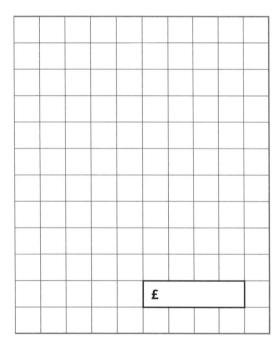

16. A rugby team of 15 players win £2000. They share the money equally between them in whole pounds and give what's left over to charity. How much is given to charity?

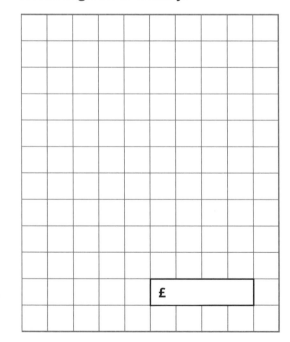

17. A teacher shares 200 sweets equally with her class, and then asks everyone to give back one sweet. If there are 25 children, how many sweets will they each take home?

18. At a concert, the total money paid to enter was £7608.
If tickets cost £12 each, how many people were there?

19. 27 children went on a school camping trip for three nights.
If they paid £769.50 altogether, how much did each night cost per child?

£

CAN YOU?

☐ Use estimation to check answers.

☐ Decide on an appropriate degree of accuracy for a problem.

☐ Understand and use the inverse relationships between addition and subtraction and between multiplication and division to check answers where possible.

SKILLS CHECK

Estimating is useful to get a quick idea for calculations. It can also help you see if your calculations are 'about right'.

Use rounding to help you estimate.

304 + 295 is approximately 600.
This is almost 300 + 300. The first number is 4 more and the second is 5 less, so changes for the approximate numbers almost balance.

5940 + 3100 is approximately 9000.
We know that 5000 + 3000 is 8000, and that 900 + 100 = 1000.

45,680 + 23,095 is approximately 69,000.
We know that 45,000 + 23,000 equals 68,000, and that the other parts are greater than 500. For 5 and above we round up, so we can add on an extra 1000 to get 69,000.

Using **inverses** is a great way of checking calculations. Inverse means 'opposite' or 'reverse'. Addition and subtraction are inverses. Multiplication and division are inverses. Look at these examples.

1. 385 + 227 = 612

Using an inverse calculation to check, we can either do 612 − 385, or 612 − 227.

	$^5\cancel{6}$	$^{10}\cancel{1}$	12
−	2	2	7
	3	8	5

So the original calculation is correct.

2. 23 × 65 = 1495

A long division can help us check. We use 23 to divide 1495 because it is easier.

					6	5
2	3	1	4	9	5	
	−	1	3	8		
			1	1	5	
		−	1	1	5	
					0	

So the original calculation is correct.

PRACTICE

1. Say if each of these estimates is right or wrong, and explain why.

   a. 211 + 53 = 270, to the nearest 10

   _____

   _____

   b. 2845 + 3140 = 5000, to the nearest 1000

   _____

   _____

   c. 2,100,000 + 1,400,000 = 4,000,000, to the nearest 1,000,000

   _____

   _____

2. Circle the nearest estimate for each calculation.

   a. 145 + 131 to the nearest 10:   **b.** 6439 + 2395 to the nearest 100:

     270   280   290   300   8700   8800   8900   9000

   c. 63,790 + 22,187 to the nearest 10,000:   **d.** 283,500 − 172,390 to the nearest 100,000:

    60,000   70,000   80,000   90,000   0   100,000   200,000   400,000

3. Use an inverse calculation to check each of these calculations, and then mark them right or wrong.

   a. 47 + 35 = 82   ☐   **b.** 98 − 39 = 59   ☐

   c. 325 − 67 = 257   ☐   **d.** 217 + 156 = 373   ☐

4. Jenny says 856 ÷ 12 = 73

   Use an inverse calculation to say if she is right or wrong.

   Jenny is _____ .

CAN YOU?

☐ Use common factors to simplify fractions.

☐ Compare fractions by giving them common denominators.

☐ Order fractions according to size.

☐ Change improper fractions to mixed numbers, and vice versa.

SKILLS CHECK

To **simplify** a fraction, divide the numerator (top number) and denominator (bottom number) by a common factor.

6 out of 8 squares are shaded, or $\frac{3}{4}$

$\frac{4}{10} = \frac{2}{5}$ (Divide top and bottom by 2)

$\frac{45}{100} = \frac{9}{20}$ (Divide top and bottom by 5)

Or divide the numerator and denominator by more than one common factor.

$\frac{90}{150} = \frac{45}{75}$ (Divide top and bottom by 2)

$\frac{45}{75} = \frac{9}{15}$ (Divide top and bottom by 5)

then $\frac{9}{15} = \frac{3}{5}$ (Divide top and bottom by 3)

The original fraction and its simplified version are **equivalent fractions**.

To **compare fractions** they must have the same denominator – the **lowest common denominator**. To compare $\frac{3}{5}$ and $\frac{2}{3}$, the lowest common denominator is: 5 × 3 = 15

$\frac{2}{3} = \frac{10}{15}$ (Multiply top and bottom by 5)

$\frac{3}{5} = \frac{9}{15}$ (Multiply top and bottom by 3)

$\frac{10}{15} > \frac{9}{15}$, so $\frac{2}{3} > \frac{3}{5}$

Improper fractions have a larger numerator than denominator. They are larger than one. They can be converted to mixed numbers by dividing the denominator into the numerator.

$\frac{3}{2} = 1\frac{1}{2}$ $\frac{14}{6} = 2\frac{2}{6} = 2\frac{1}{3}$ $\frac{21}{4} = 5\frac{1}{4}$

Mixed numbers are converted to improper fractions by changing the whole number into a fraction.

$3\frac{1}{5} = \frac{15}{5} + \frac{1}{5} = \frac{16}{5}$ $2\frac{3}{4} = \frac{8}{4} + \frac{3}{4} = \frac{11}{4}$

To compare a mixed number and an improper fraction, we still need a common denominator.

Which is bigger, $6\frac{2}{5}$ or $\frac{20}{3}$?

$6\frac{2}{5} = \frac{30}{5} + \frac{2}{5} = \frac{32}{5}$

Multiplying top and bottom by 3 gives $\frac{96}{15}$

Multiplying $\frac{20}{3}$ top and bottom by 5 gives $\frac{100}{15}$

So, $\frac{20}{3} > 6\frac{2}{5}$

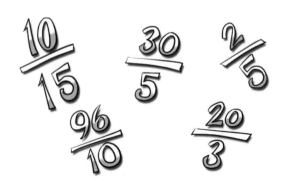

PRACTICE

1. Insert the correct sign between the fractions in each pair. Choose from =, < or >.

a. $\frac{1}{3}$ ☐ $\frac{4}{12}$ **b.** $\frac{5}{6}$ ☐ $\frac{2}{3}$ **c.** $\frac{3}{4}$ ☐ $\frac{9}{12}$ **d.** $\frac{5}{10}$ ☐ $\frac{3}{5}$

e. $\frac{1}{2}$ ☐ $\frac{8}{16}$ **f.** $\frac{2}{9}$ ☐ $\frac{5}{18}$ **g.** $\frac{2}{3}$ ☐ $\frac{3}{5}$ **h.** $\frac{5}{7}$ ☐ $\frac{3}{4}$

2. Rearrange each set of fractions in order from smallest to largest.

a. $\frac{12}{20}$ $\frac{1}{2}$ $\frac{6}{8}$ $\frac{3}{10}$ $\frac{4}{5}$ _____

b. $\frac{2}{3}$ $\frac{3}{4}$ $\frac{5}{6}$ $\frac{7}{12}$ $\frac{1}{2}$ _____

c. $\frac{8}{15}$ $\frac{3}{5}$ $\frac{2}{3}$ $\frac{4}{10}$ $\frac{1}{2}$ _____

d. $\frac{3}{20}$ $\frac{7}{60}$ $\frac{2}{15}$ $\frac{1}{10}$ $\frac{2}{30}$ _____

3. Match each improper fraction to its mixed number equivalent.

$\boxed{\frac{5}{2}}$ $\boxed{\frac{8}{3}}$ $\boxed{\frac{15}{4}}$ $\boxed{\frac{16}{5}}$ $\boxed{\frac{21}{5}}$ $\boxed{\frac{21}{4}}$ $\boxed{\frac{7}{2}}$ $\boxed{\frac{19}{8}}$

$\boxed{2\frac{2}{3}}$ $\boxed{3\frac{1}{2}}$ $\boxed{3\frac{1}{5}}$ $\boxed{5\frac{1}{4}}$ $\boxed{2\frac{1}{2}}$ $\boxed{2\frac{3}{8}}$ $\boxed{4\frac{1}{5}}$ $\boxed{3\frac{3}{4}}$

4. Insert the correct sign between each pair of improper fractions and mixed numbers. Choose from =, < or >.

a. $\frac{4}{3}$ ☐ $1\frac{1}{4}$ **b.** $2\frac{1}{2}$ ☐ $\frac{10}{4}$ **c.** $\frac{12}{5}$ ☐ $2\frac{3}{10}$ **d.** $\frac{15}{6}$ ☐ $3\frac{2}{3}$

e. $\frac{4}{3}$ ☐ $1\frac{1}{2}$ **f.** $5\frac{1}{4}$ ☐ $\frac{28}{5}$ **g.** $3\frac{2}{5}$ ☐ $\frac{34}{10}$ **h.** $4\frac{5}{6}$ ☐ $\frac{57}{12}$

5. Arrange the fractions in each group.

a. In ascending order: $\frac{13}{3}$ $3\frac{2}{3}$ $\frac{23}{16}$ $3\frac{1}{6}$ _____

b. In descending order: $\frac{27}{10}$ $2\frac{4}{5}$ $3\frac{1}{2}$ $\frac{12}{5}$ _____

CAN YOU?

 Convert fractions to have common denominators.

 Add and subtract fractions.

Add and subtract mixed numbers.

SKILLS CHECK

To add two or more fractions, they must have the same **denominator**. You need to find the **lowest common multiple** for the denominators. Only add the **numerators**.

$\frac{1}{2} + \frac{1}{4}$

4 is the lowest common multiple for 2 and 4, so you must change the denominator of $\frac{1}{2}$. Multiply the numerator and the denominator by the same number.

$\frac{1 \times 2 = 2}{2 \times 2 = 4}$

So, $\frac{1}{2} + \frac{1}{4} = \frac{2}{4} + \frac{1}{4} = \frac{3}{4}$

$\frac{3}{5} + \frac{1}{3}$

These fractions have different denominators and neither of them is a multiple of the other. You must change both of the fractions to ensure they have the same denominator.
$3 \times 5 = 15$, so multiply $\frac{3}{5}$ by 3 and $\frac{1}{3}$ by 5 then add the result.

$\frac{3}{5} + \frac{1}{3} = \frac{3 \times 3}{5 \times 3} + \frac{1 \times 5}{3 \times 5}$

$= \frac{9}{15} + \frac{5}{15} = \frac{14}{15}$

To subtract fractions, just change them to give each the same denominator (just like adding), and then subtract one numerator from the other. Look at these examples.

$\frac{1}{2} - \frac{1}{6} = \frac{1 \times 3}{2 \times 3} - \frac{1}{6} = \frac{3}{6} - \frac{1}{6} = \frac{2}{6}$ or $\frac{1}{3}$

$\frac{3}{5} - \frac{1}{3} = \frac{3 \times 3}{5 \times 3} - \frac{1 \times 5}{3 \times 5} = \frac{9}{15} - \frac{5}{15} = \frac{4}{15}$

For **mixed numbers**, add the whole numbers and the fraction parts separately, or change both to improper fractions.

$3\frac{1}{2} + 4\frac{1}{6}$ $\quad = 3 + 4 + \frac{1}{2} + \frac{1}{6}$

$= 7 + \frac{3}{6} + \frac{1}{6}$

$= 7 + \frac{4}{6}$

$= 7\frac{4}{6}$

$3\frac{1}{4} - 2\frac{5}{6}$ $\quad = \frac{13}{4} - \frac{17}{6}$

$= \frac{39}{12} - \frac{34}{12}$

$= \frac{5}{12}$

PRACTICE

1. Answer these questions.

   a. $\frac{1}{5} + \frac{2}{5} =$ _____

   b. $\frac{3}{6} + \frac{2}{6} =$ _____

   c. $\frac{6}{7} - \frac{5}{7} =$ _____

   d. $\frac{7}{10} - \frac{5}{10} =$ _____

2. Add these fractions.

   a. $\frac{2}{5} + \frac{1}{3} =$ _____

   b. $\frac{1}{2} + \frac{1}{7} =$ _____

   c. $\frac{5}{6} + \frac{1}{2} =$ _____

   d. $\frac{1}{4} + \frac{3}{8} + \frac{1}{16} =$ _____

3. Subtract these fractions.

   a. $\frac{1}{2} - \frac{1}{4} =$ _____

   b. $\frac{5}{6} - \frac{2}{3} =$ _____

   c. $\frac{1}{6} - \frac{1}{10} =$ _____

   d. $\frac{7}{8} - \frac{1}{4} =$ _____

4. Add these mixed numbers.

   a. $3\frac{1}{6} + 2\frac{2}{3} =$ _____

   b. $3\frac{7}{10} + 5\frac{8}{15} =$ _____

5. Subtract these mixed numbers.

   a. $3\frac{2}{3} - 1\frac{1}{6} =$ _____

   b. $1\frac{3}{8} - \frac{2}{3} =$ _____

6. If I eat $2\frac{1}{2}$ cupcakes for lunch and $1\frac{3}{4}$ for tea, how many will I have eaten altogether?

CAN YOU?

☐ Find fractions of quantities.

☐ Multiply a fraction or whole number by another fraction.

SKILLS CHECK

To multiply fractions, multiply the numerators together, and then multiply the denominators together.

$$\frac{1}{2} \times \frac{1}{4} = \frac{1}{8}$$

Notice how the answer is smaller than both the original fractions.

Here's another example.

$$\frac{2}{9} \times \frac{3}{4} = \frac{2 \times 3}{9 \times 4} = \frac{6}{36} = \frac{1}{6}$$

To multiply a fraction by a whole number, just convert the whole number into a fraction by giving it a denominator of 1. (**Remember:** any whole number is a fraction with a denominator of 1.)

Tina has 50 marbles. She gives three-fifths of them to Jen. How many does she have left?

$$\frac{3}{5} \times \frac{50}{1} = \frac{150}{5} = \frac{30}{1}$$

So if she gives 30 to Jen, Tina must have 20 marbles left.

Division is like multiplying by a fraction. For example, you can write $30 \div 5$ as $\frac{1}{5}$ of 30 and therefore as:

$$\frac{1}{5} \times 30 = \frac{30}{5} = \frac{6}{1} = 6$$

'What is $\frac{1}{3} \div 2$?' is the same as saying 'What is $\frac{1}{2}$ of $\frac{1}{3}$?' You can write this as:

$$\frac{1}{2} \times \frac{1}{3} = \frac{1 \times 1}{2 \times 3} = \frac{1}{6}$$

So, $\frac{1}{3} \div 2 = \frac{1}{6}$

Here is another example:

$\frac{3}{4} \div 5$ is the same as $\frac{1}{5} \times \frac{3}{4} = \frac{1 \times 3}{5 \times 4} = \frac{3}{20}$

When multiplying mixed numbers, you need to convert them into improper fractions first. Look at these examples.

$\frac{1}{4} \times 2\frac{1}{5}$

$= \frac{1}{4} \times \frac{11}{5}$ (2 wholes is $\frac{10}{5}$)

$= \frac{11}{20}$ ($1 \times 11 = 11$, $4 \times 5 = 20$)

$2\frac{1}{3} \times 3\frac{1}{2}$

$= \frac{7}{3} \times \frac{7}{2}$ (2 wholes are $\frac{6}{3}$, 3 wholes are $\frac{6}{2}$)

$= \frac{49}{6}$ ($7 \times 7 = 49$, $3 \times 2 = 6$)

$= 8\frac{1}{6}$ ($\frac{49}{6}$ can be simplified, $8 \times 6 = 48$, with $\frac{1}{6}$ left over)

PRACTICE

1. Multiply these fractions.

   a. $\frac{1}{4} \times \frac{1}{3} =$ _____

   b. $\frac{1}{4} \times \frac{8}{9} =$ _____

2. Multiply these whole numbers.

   a. $3 \times 2\frac{1}{6} =$ _____

   b. $\frac{1}{5} \times 10 =$ _____

3. Divide these fractions.

   a. $\frac{1}{2} \div 2 =$ _____

   b. $\frac{4}{5} \div 8 =$ _____

4. A quarter of the cars in the school car park are silver. There are 24 cars altogether. How many cars are silver?

5. A pack of butter weighs 500 grams. Johnny needs 200 grams to make biscuits. What fraction of the butter does he need?

6. A greedy dad eats $\frac{4}{7}$ of a bag of popcorn, and the rest is shared between 3 children. What fraction of the bag of popcorn will each child receive?

7. A farmer grows potatoes. There are 1000 potatoes in a field. If $\frac{3}{8}$ of the potatoes are not suitable for eating, how many can be eaten?

CAN YOU?

☐ Read and write numbers with up to three decimal places.

☐ Identify the value of each digit in a decimal.

☐ Compare and order decimals.

☐ Round numbers to one, two or three decimal places.

☐ Solve practical problems involving decimals.

☐ Multiply and divide numbers by 10, 100 and 1000 and give answers up to three decimal places.

☐ Multiply numbers with up to two decimal places by whole numbers.

☐ Use written division methods for calculating answers up to two decimal places.

SKILLS CHECK

A **decimal** is the fraction part of a number, the part of one whole.
One tenth is $\frac{1}{10}$. One hundredth is $\frac{1}{100}$. One thousandth is $\frac{1}{1000}$.
There are 10 one-hundredths in one tenth, and 10 one-thousandths in one hundredth.

Look at the number 9145.237 in the place-value table.

1000s	100s	10s	1s	0.1s	0.01s	0.001s
9	1	4	5	2	3	7

This number is nine thousand, one hundred and forty-five **point** two three seven. In this number, there are **2 tenths**, **3 hundredths** and **7 thousandths**.

You can **round decimals** just like whole numbers.

0.125 rounds up to 0.13 to two decimal places, and rounds down to 0.1 for just one decimal place.

When **adding and subtracting decimals**, use the same rules as whole numbers – just make sure you line up the decimal point.

Multiplying and dividing uses the same rules as whole numbers, just think carefully about where the decimal point should be. Remember, when you multiply and divide numbers by powers of 10, all the digits move one place for each power of 10.

23 ÷ 100 = 0.23   0.15 × 100 = 15   43 ÷ 1000 = 0.043   0.08 × 1000 = 80

Money calculations often involve decimals to two decimal places (pounds and pence). You may also need to do one or more calculations using the four operations. Think carefully about what the question is asking you and show your method.

PRACTICE

1. In each of these decimals, write the value of the underlined digit in words.

a. 0.<u>7</u>34 _____

b. 5.<u>1</u>03 _____

c. 3.64<u>9</u> _____

d. 3.0<u>5</u>2 _____

e. 12.<u>4</u>11 _____

f. 6.38<u>7</u> _____

2. Round these decimals.

a. 2.36 to one decimal place = _____

b. 0.434 to two decimal places = _____

c. 1.65 to one decimal place = _____

d. 3.119 to two decimal places = _____

e. 4.82 to one decimal place = _____

f. 0.775 to two decimal places = _____

3. Position these decimals on the number lines.

a. 0.1, 0.8, 0.75, 0.35

0 ——————————————————————— 1

b. 0.21, 0.25, 0.215, 0.288

0.2 ——————————————————————— 0.3

c. 0.615, 0.611, 0.610, 0.619

0.61 ——————————————————————— 0.62

4. Complete these decimal sequences.

a. 0.6   0.8   1.0   1.2   _____   _____

b. 0.12   0.15   0.18   0.21   _____   _____

c. 1.955   1.95   1.945   1.94   _____   _____

5. Complete these calculations.

a. 47 ÷ 100 = _____

b. 1.28 × 1000 = _____

c. 0.034 × 10 = _____

d. 7 ÷ 1000 = _____

6. Complete these calculations, write your answers as decimals.

a.

	0 .	4	6	3
+	0 .	3	3	5

b.

	0 .	4	6	3
×				5

c.

	0 .	7	4	3
−	0 .	3	2	5

d.

	1 .	4	5	5
−	0 .	7	2	5

e.

	3 .	5	1	3
	0 .	8	0	7
+	0 .	3	9	4

f.

	0 .	4	6	3
×			1	2

g.

8	3	0	0	0

h.

7	1	2 .	5	0	9

7. Priya makes some improvements to her bicycle. A new bell costs £4.65 and a new mudguard costs £11.49. How much does she spend altogether?

£ _____

8. Tom spends £12.36 at the supermarket. How much change will he get from a £20 note?

£ _____

9. School meals cost £2.45 each. What will the cost be for five meals?

£ _____

10. Six children each give the same amount of money to a charity. If the total amount is £19.44, calculate how much each child gave.

£ _____

11. A family of two adults and three children go to see a film. Cinema tickets cost £8.75 per adult and £5.25 per child. How much change will they get from £40?

£ _____

12. Pineapples cost £1.59 each, mangoes cost £0.79 each. Three children together buy one pineapple and three mangoes. They share the cost equally. How much does each child pay?

£ _____

CAN YOU?

- [ ] Recognise and use equivalences between fractions, decimals and percentages.
- [ ] Calculate decimal fraction equivalents for simple fractions.
- [ ] Multiply and divide numbers by 100 to convert percentages to decimals and vice versa.

SKILLS CHECK

Per cent means out of 100. 100 per cent is one whole. 50% is half.

Any fraction can also be written as a percentage or as a decimal.

You can convert between fractions, decimals and percentages to find **equivalent** values.

Learn these equivalent values by heart.

Fraction	Decimal	Percentage
$\frac{1}{1}$	1.0	100%
$\frac{1}{2}$	0.5	50%
$\frac{1}{4}$	0.25	25%
$\frac{1}{3}$	0.333	33.3%
$\frac{3}{4}$	0.75	75%
$\frac{1}{5}$	0.2	20%
$\frac{1}{10}$	0.1	10%
$\frac{1}{100}$	0.01	1%
$\frac{1}{1000}$	0.001	0.1%

The decimal and percentage equivalents for $\frac{1}{3}$ are approximations only.

You can arrange fractions, percentages and decimals in order.

Arrange these in ascending order: 35%, 0.42, $\frac{3}{4}$
You need to change the amounts to equivalents to compare them.

To make them all percentages:
To convert a decimal to a percentage, multiply it by 100. 0.42 → 0.42 × 100 → 42%

To convert a fraction to a percentage, change it to decimal, then multiply it by 100.

$\frac{3}{4}$ → 0.75 × 100 = 75%
So you get 35%, 42% and 75%

To make them all decimals:
To convert a percentage to a decimal, divide it by 100. 35% → $\frac{35}{100}$ = 0.35

To convert a fraction to a decimal you must divide it.
$\frac{3}{4}$ = 3 ÷ 4 = 0.75
So you get 0.35, 0.42 and 0.75

To make them all fractions:
To convert a percentage to a fraction, remove the percentage sign, give it a denominator of 100 and then, if possible, simplify it.

35% → $\frac{35}{100}$ = $\frac{7}{20}$ *(divide top and bottom by 5)*
To convert a decimal to a fraction, write it as a percentage over 100.

0.45 → $\frac{45}{100}$ = $\frac{9}{20}$
So you get $\frac{7}{20}$, $\frac{9}{20}$ and $\frac{3}{4}$ (or $\frac{15}{20}$)

All allow you to order the amounts to: 35%, 0.42, $\frac{3}{4}$

PRACTICE

1. Arrange these fractions, decimals and percentages in order, from smallest to largest.

a. 50% $\frac{1}{4}$ 0.1 0.9 _____

b. $\frac{1}{3}$ 25% 0.2 0.4 _____

c. $\frac{4}{5}$ 65% 0.7 $\frac{2}{3}$ _____

d. 10% $\frac{1}{8}$ 0.075 7% _____

2. Draw lines to match equivalent decimals, fractions and percentages.

a.		**b.**		**c.**		
0.1	45%	10%	0.75	$\frac{1}{10}$	0.2	25%
0.5	$\frac{1}{10}$	35%	$\frac{7}{20}$	$\frac{1}{5}$	0.333	10%
0.45	100%	75%	$\frac{9}{10}$	$\frac{1}{4}$	0.1	33%
1.0	$\frac{1}{2}$	90%	0.1	$\frac{1}{3}$	0.25	20%

3. Complete this chart.

Fraction	$\frac{1}{2}$	$\frac{1}{4}$		$\frac{3}{4}$		$\frac{1}{10}$	$\frac{1}{100}$		$\frac{5}{100}$	$\frac{5}{1000}$
Decimal	0.5		0.333	0.75	0.2	0.1		0.001		
Per cent		25%	33.3%		20%		1%	0.1%		

4. Convert these decimals to percentages.

a. 0.2 _____   **b.** 0.25 _____   **c.** 0.47 _____

d. 0.333 _____   **e.** 0.98 _____   **f.** 0.02 _____

5. Convert these percentages to decimals.

a. 78% _____   **b.** 47% _____   **c.** 1% _____

d. 99% _____   **e.** 66.6% _____   **f.** 50% _____

CAN YOU?

- [ ] Solve problems using ratios and proportions.
- [ ] Solve problems by calculating percentages of quantities.

- [ ] Use percentages for comparison.
- [ ] Solve problems involving unequal quantities.
- [ ] Solve problems involving unequal sharing and grouping.

SKILLS CHECK

Proportions show us the fraction of the whole.

1 in 8 cubes is grey, or $\frac{1}{8}$, 0.125 or 12.5%.
2 in 8 cubes are black, or $\frac{2}{8}$, $\frac{1}{4}$, 0.25 or 25%.
5 in 8 cubes are white, or $\frac{5}{8}$, 0.625 or 62.5%.

Ratios compare parts of a whole.

There is 1 blue cube for every 2 red cubes.
The ratio of blue to red is 1 to 2 or 1:2.

If a bag contains 80 blue, red and yellow cubes where the proportion of blue cubes is $\frac{1}{8}$, red cubes $\frac{1}{4}$ and yellow cubes $\frac{5}{8}$, then:

- The number of blue cubes = $\frac{1}{8} \times 80 = 10$
- The number of red cubes = $\frac{1}{4} \times 80 = 20$
- The number of yellow cubes = $\frac{5}{8} \times 80 = 50$

The ratios would be:
Blue cubes to red cubes = 10 to 20 = 1 to 2
Red cubes to blue cubes = 20 to 10 = 2 to 1
Yellow cubes to red cubes = 50 to 20 = 5 to 2
(Divide both numbers in the ratio by a common factor.)

Percentages of a quantity

To calculate a percentage of a quantity, either multiply by the fraction or the decimal, or use a mental method. Look at this example.

Find 25% of 200.
Using a fraction: $\frac{25}{100} \times 200 = 50$
Using a decimal: $0.25 \times 200 = 50$
Using a mental method:
10% of 200 = 20, so 25% = 20 + 20 + 10 = 50

Compare percentages

You can compare using percentages. Look at this example.

40% of a class of 30 children prefer pizza, and 50% of a class of 22 children prefer pizza. Which class has more children who prefer pizza?

In the first class, 40% of 30 = 12.
In the second class, 50% of 22 = 11.
So the first class has more pizza lovers, even though a smaller percentage of the class prefer pizza.

The topping on a vegetarian pizza is made using two mushrooms and one tomato. How many pizzas can you make with 20 mushrooms? How many tomatoes do you need?

If we have 20 mushrooms, we can make a maximum of 20 ÷ 2 = 10 pizzas.
We would need 10 × 1 = 10 tomatoes for these pizzas.

Some problems involve unequal sharing or grouping. Look at this example.

$\frac{2}{3}$ *of a class of children are girls.*
If there are 12 boys in the class, calculate how many children there are in total.

If $\frac{2}{3}$ of the class are girls, then $\frac{1}{3}$ must be boys.
So, $\frac{1}{3}$ of the total number of children is 12.
$\frac{3}{3}$ is a whole, so 3 × 12 = 36 children.

PRACTICE

1. What is the proportion of each type of bead in the bag? Give your answers as decimals.

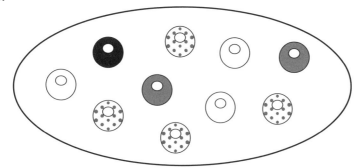

   a. black beads _____   **b.** white beads _____

   c. spotty beads _____   **d.** grey beads _____

2. Another bag of beads contains 40 black, white, spotty and grey beads in the same ratios as the bag in question 1. Calculate how many beads there are of each type.

   a. black beads _____   **b.** white beads _____

   c. spotty beads _____   **d.** grey beads _____

3. Calculate these percentages.

   a. 20% of 80 = _____   **b.** 95% of 120 = _____

   c. 50% of 2500 = _____   **d.** 35% of 3200 = _____

4. Solve these ratio and proportion problems.

   a. In a recipe for cakes there must be 1 egg for every 200g of flour. If Zac uses 6 eggs, how much flour will he need?

   b. If a car travels 40 miles for every gallon of petrol it uses, how much fuel will it use on a 250 mile journey?

5. Solve this percentage problem.
   A book shop gives a 20% discount if someone buys 5 books. Hanmo buys three books for £5.99 and two for £6.99. How much will she pay altogether?

   £ _____

CAN YOU?

 Solve problems involving similar shapes where the scale factor is known.

SKILLS CHECK

Scale factors are used for enlarging or reducing lines, shapes and objects.

This line is 2cm long. _____

If you increase it by a scale factor of 3, then for every 1cm of the original line, you must draw 3cm for the enlarged line. Enlarged by a scale factor of 3 the new line will be 2cm × 3 = 6cm.

_____

You can do this with shapes too. This rectangle has been enlarged by a scale factor of 3.

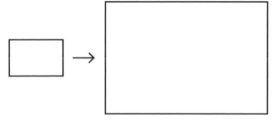

The length of each side has been multiplied by 3. Notice that the angles stay the same. When one shape is an enlargement of another, we say that the shapes are similar. Look at these two similar shapes.

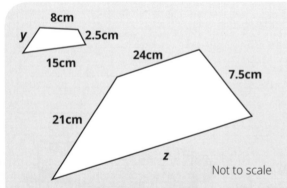

Not to scale

Compare the lengths of matching sides to work out the scale factor.

8cm → 24cm   24 ÷ 8 = 3
2.5cm → 7.5cm   7.5 ÷ 2.5 = 3
The scale factor is 3.

15cm → z
15cm × scale factor = 15cm × 3 = 45cm
Length z is 45cm

y → 21cm
21cm ÷ scale factor = 21cm ÷ 3 = 7cm
Length y is 7cm

You can also use scale factors to reduce the size of things. Look at this example.

Ayshani drew a scale drawing of her bedroom. 1cm on her plan represents 2m in real life. The scale factor is 200 (2m = 200cm). On the plan, the length of the bedroom is 7cm. How long is the bedroom is in real life?
The actual bedroom is 7cm × 200 = 1400cm = 14m.

In real life, the bedroom is 9m wide. How wide is the bedroom on the plan?
On the plan, the width of the bedroom is 9m ÷ 200 = 900cm ÷ 200 = 4.5cm.

Sometimes, you will see the scale factor written as a scale on a map. 1:200 is another way of saying that 1cm on a map is 200cm = 2m in real life.

PRACTICE

1. Write the scale factor of each enlargement.

a. ▬ ⟶ ▬▬▬▬▬ _____

b. ▬ ⟶ ▬▬▬ _____

c. ▬ ⟶ ▬▬▬▬▬▬▬ _____

d. ▬ ⟶ ▪ _____

2. Solve these problems.

a. Shape B is an enlargement of shape A.
What is the scale factor?

_____

b. A building is 80 metres high. Nina makes a model where
1cm represents 2m. What height will the model be?

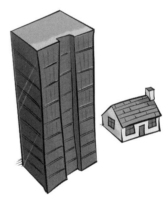

_____

Nina makes a model of a house to the same scale.
If her model is 5cm tall, what is the actual height
of the house?

_____

3. The diagram shows two similar triangles.

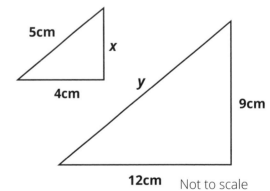

5cm

x

4cm

y

9cm

12cm   Not to scale

a. What is the scale factor? _____

b. How long is *x*? _____

c. How long is *y*? _____

4. Tom draws a square and labels it A.
He uses the side lengths of A and the scale factor 0.5 to draw B.
He uses the side lengths of A and the scale factor 3 to draw C.

What is the scale factor that enlarges square B to square C? _____

CAN YOU?

☐ Use simple formulae.

☐ Use algebra to make and describe number sequences.

SKILLS CHECK

Algebra uses letters in place of numbers. We call the letters **unknowns** if you do not know their value, but you can often work them out.

If $6 + a = 10$, a must be equal to 4 because $6 + 4 = 10$.

Formulae use letters to represent unknowns that can vary in value. These are called **variables**.

If a truffle costs 30p and a bag costs 25p, the total cost can be calculated using this formula:
$C = N \times 30p + 25p$
C = the total cost; N = the number of truffles
So, if someone wanted five truffles, the cost would be $C = 5 \times 30p + 25p = 175p$ or £1.75
In the formula, C and N are variables, and the 25p is a **constant**.

Sometimes you need to rearrange the formula. **Remember:** whatever you do to one side you must do to the other.

If you need to work out the value of N in:
$345 = 30N + 15$
You can write the equation the other way around: $30N + 15 = 345$
Next, subtract 15 from each side: $30N = 330$
Finally, divide each side by 30: $N = 11$
So 11 truffles were bought.

For some problems you need to create your own **formula**. For example:

A casserole recipe says to cook for 30 minutes per kilogram, and add an extra 10 minutes. A formula to calculate the total time might have T for time and W for weight, and a constant of 10 for the extra 10 minutes: $T = 30W + 10$

Number sequences always have a formula, which helps us to calculate the next term.

Term	1	2	3	4	5
Number	5	7	9	11	13

Each term in this sequence = $2n + 3$, where n is the term value.

So, the 20th term would be $2 \times 20 + 3 = 43$. The nth term is $2n + 3$.

Work out the formula for the nth term of this sequence.

Term	1	2	3	4	5
Number	6	10	14	18	22

The numbers are increasing by 4 each time. Work out the constant by taking 4 away from the first number = $6 - 4 = 2$.

So the sequence is ?n + 2

To give 6 as the first term, it must be: 4n + 2
Check this for the other numbers in the sequence to show that it works.

 **PRACTICE**

1. A window cleaner charges £2 per window plus a £5 call-out charge. Using the formula $c = 2w + 5$, calculate the cost of cleaning.

   a. 2 windows: _____ **b.** 13 windows: _____

2. A farmer estimates the time to shear sheep is 30 minutes per sheep plus 45 minutes clearing-up time. Using the formula $t = 30s + 45$, calculate the time it takes to shear.

   a. 5 sheep: _____ mins **b.** 20 sheep: _____ mins

3. Solve this problem. A taxi meter is set for a basic cost of £3, plus £2 for every mile travelled.

   a. Write a formula that can be used to calculate the cost of any journey.

   _____

   b. How much will a 12-mile journey cost?

   _____

4. When you convert temperature measured in Centigrade to Fahrenheit, you use the formula $F = \frac{9C}{5} + 32$. Use the formula to convert these temperatures.

   a. 5°C = _____ °F

   b. 20°C = _____ °F

5. When you convert temperature measured in Fahrenheit to Centigrade, you use the formula $C = \frac{5}{9} \times (F - 32)$. Use the formula to convert these temperatures.

   a. 59°F = _____°C **b.** 122°F = _____ °C

6. Complete these sequences.

   a. 4, 7, 10, 13, _____, _____ **b.** 1, 8, 15, 22, _____, _____

7. Draw lines to match the sequences to the correct expressions.

   | 1, 3, 5, 7, 9 … | | 1, 4, 9, 16, … | | 4, 7, 10, 13, … | | −2, −1, 0, 1, … |

   | n^2 | | $3n + 1$ | | $2n − 1$ | | $n − 3$ |

CAN YOU?

☐ Solve equations that have one unknown term or a missing number.

☐ Find pairs of numbers in equations that have two unknowns.

☐ List all the possible answers for equations with two unknowns.

SKILLS CHECK

This problem has one unknown and you can solve it mentally.

$c + 7 = 10$ $c = 3$ because $3 + 7 = 10$

Questions could use any letter or an empty box to show a missing number.

Some equations are more complicated, and you have to rearrange the calculation to have the unknown on its own on one side of the equals sign.

$$2p - 7 = 15$$
$$2p - 7 + 7 = 15 + 7$$
$$2p = 22$$
$$2p \div 2 = 22 \div 2$$
$$p = 11$$

Notice how the problem is always balanced. You must do exactly the same thing to each side, one step at a time.

Equations with two unknowns are more complicated. The unknowns are called variables and they can have more than one value.

$s + t = 4$
If s and t are both whole, positive numbers, you can have:
$1 + 3 = 4$ $s = 1, t = 3$
$2 + 2 = 4$ $s = 2, t = 2$
$3 + 1 = 4$ $s = 3, t = 1$
There are three possible solutions.

For some equations there are lots of possibilities.

If $j + k = 9$, and j and k are whole numbers, list all the possible values for each variable.

Draw a table and work out the possibilities and write them in it, starting with j = 0. Then list your values neatly.

j	0	1	2	3	4	5	6	7	8	9
k	9	8	7	6	5	4	3	2	1	0

PRACTICE

1. Find the value of the letter in each equation.

   a. $p + 6 = 9$ $p =$ _____

   b. $16 - d = 4$ $d =$ _____

   c. $27 = 12 + t$ $t =$ _____

   d. $z^2 - 5 = 11$ $z =$ _____

2. Find the value of the letter in each equation.

   a. $3y = 18$ $y =$ _____

   b. $32 = 8w$ $w =$ _____

   c. $\frac{d}{4} = 7$ $d =$ _____

   d. $\frac{n}{3} = 9$ $n =$ _____

3. Find the missing numbers.

   a. ☐ $+ 2 = 5$

   b. ☐ $- 5 = 32$

   c. $4 +$ ☐ $= 20$

   d. ☐ $\times 3 = 39$

   e. ☐ $\div 5 = 3$

   f. $6 \times$ ☐ $= 36$

4. Find the values for the two unknowns in each equation. Answers must be positive whole numbers only.

   a. $r + s = 6$

r	0	1	2	3	4	5	6
s							

   b. $2c + d = 12$

c							
d							

   c. $3g - h = 15$

g	5	6	7	8	9	10	11
h							

   d. $y + 3z = 20$

y							
z							

5. Make *p* the subject of each of these equations.

   a. $p + q = 9$ $p =$ _____

   b. $9 = p + 3m$ $p =$ _____

   c. $3b - p = t$ $p =$ _____

6. A family spent £30 on tickets for a football match.
   If adult tickets cost £10 and child tickets cost £5 each, write down the possible combinations of adults and children who went to the match.

Number of adults				
Number of children				

 CAN YOU?

- [ ] Read, write and covert between standard units for length, mass, capacity and time.

- [ ] Convert between miles and kilometres.

- [ ] Solve problems involving measures, using decimals where necessary.

SKILLS CHECK

Converting between units in **mass**, **capacity** and **length** involves multiplying and dividing between powers of 10.

	Example	Operation	Conversion
Converting mass	750g = ?kg	÷ 1000 (1000g = 1kg)	750g = 0.75 kg
	8.4kg = ?g	× 1000 (1kg = 1000g)	8.4kg = 8400g
Converting capacity	8000cl = ? litres	÷ 100 (100cl = 1 litre)	8000cl = 80 litres
	2000ml = ? litres	÷ 1000 (1000ml = 1 litre)	2000ml = 2 litres
	5 litres = ?cl	× 100 (1 litre = 100cl)	5 litres = 500cl
	4.6 litres = ?ml	× 1000 (1 litre = 1000ml)	4.6 litres = 4600ml
Converting time *(Remember: to convert from days to seconds, convert to hours, then minutes and then seconds. For example: 1 day = 24 × 60 × 60 = 86,400s)*	72h = ?d	÷ 24 (24h = 1d)	72h = 3d
	300 mins = ?h	÷ 60 (60 mins = 1h)	300 mins = 5h
	6000s = ? mins	÷ 60 (60s = 1 min)	6000s = 100 mins
	2d = ?h	× 24 (1 day = 24h)	2d = 48h
	8h = ? mins	× 60 (1h = 60 mins)	8h = 480 mins
	11 mins = ?s	× 60 (1 min = 60s)	11 mins = 660s
Converting length	25mm = ?cm	÷ 10 (10mm = 1cm)	25mm = 2.5cm
	367cm = ?m	÷ 100 (100cm = 1m)	367cm = 3.67m
	578m = ?km	÷ 1000 (1000m = 1km)	578m = 0.578km
	4.6cm = ?mm	× 10 (1cm = 10mm)	4.6cm = 46mm
	9.75m = ?cm	× 100 (1m = 100cm)	9.75m = 975cm
	8.4km = ?m	× 1000 (1km = 1000m)	8.4km = 8400m

Length, weight and capacity are sometimes measured in **imperial units.**

The imperial units for length are inches, feet and miles.

12 inches = 1 foot
3 feet = 1 yard
1760 yards = 1 mile

The imperial units for weight are pounds (lb), ounces (oz) and stone (st).

16oz = 1lb
14lb = 1st.

The imperial units for capacity are pints and gallons.

8 pints = 1 gallon

Sometimes, you need to convert from imperial units to metric units. These are some approximate equivalences:

1 inch is about 2.5cm
5 miles are about 8km
1lb is about 2kg
1oz is about 25g
1 pint is about $\frac{1}{2}$ litre

To **order measures** according to size, they must have the same units.
Look at these examples.

Which is bigger, 2.5kg or 2600g?

2600g = 2.6kg, so 2600kg > 2.5kg

Put these measures in order of size, smallest to largest.
1 pint $\frac{1}{4}$ litre   300ml

Convert the capacities so that they are in the same unit.
1 pint is approximately $\frac{1}{2}$ litre = 500ml
$\frac{1}{4}$ litre = 250ml
So the order is:
$\frac{1}{4}$ litre   300ml   1 pint

 PRACTICE

1. **Arrange the units in order, smallest to largest.**

   a. 1.25m   75cm   0.02km   85mm   _____

   b. 0.325kg   330g   2952g   0.295kg   _____

   c. 1.1 litres   120cl   1125ml   1.05 litres   _____

   d. $2\frac{1}{4}$h   150 mins   7200s   2h 20 mins   _____

2. **Draw lines to match the equivalent weights.**

75g	7.5kg
750g	0.075kg
7500g	75kg
75,000g	0.75kg

3. **Look at these measures in imperial units. Approximate each metric equivalent.**

   a. 10 pints = _____ litres   **b.** 20 miles = _____ km

4. **Complete these length problems.**

   a. Tina is 135cm tall and John is 1m 48cm.
   What is the difference between their heights?   _____

   Tina's little brother Milo is half her height. How tall is he?   _____

   b. Johan lives 1.5 miles from his school. He walks there and back each day.
   Calculate how far he walks in kilometres each day. (Use 1 mile = 1.61km)

   _____

   If he goes to school 5 days a week, how many km does he walk altogether?

   _____

5. **Complete these weight problems.**

   a. A feather weighs 15 grams, a flower weighs 87 grams. How much more
   does the flower weigh than the feather?

   _____

   b. A restaurant uses $\frac{3}{4}$ of a 5kg sack of potatoes.
   What weight of potatoes is left over?   _____

   The chef divides the remaining potatoes into two equal piles.
   What will be the weight of each pile, in grams?   _____

6. **Complete these capacity problems.**

   a. A measuring cylinder is filled with water up to 750ml mark.
   If 300ml are poured out of it, where will the new level of water be?
   Mark this on the diagram and write the new level in ml.

   How much water would be needed to fill the cylinder to its maximum limit?

   _____

b. A fizzy drink is sold in 2-litre bottles. At the end of term party, the teacher shares a bottle between the class. If there are 25 children in the class, how much will they each receive?

_____

c. A bathtub holds 500 litres. If it is $\frac{3}{4}$ full, how much water is in it?   _____

7. **Complete these time problems.**

a. A school day starts at 8:55am, and finishes at 3:15pm.
How long does it last?   _____

Morning break is 10:30 until 10:45
Lunch break is 12:30 until 13:20
Afternoon break is 14:05 until 14:10
How long do the children have in breaks altogether?   _____

b. Karen and Frieda are friends. Karen was born at noon on March 25th 2009. Frieda was also born at noon, but a few weeks later on May 2nd 2009.

How many days older is Frieda?   _____

How long is this in hours?   _____

c. The two halves of a football match each lasts 45 minutes. How long is a match, in seconds?

_____

The half-time break lasts 10 minutes. A game starts at 19:30. There is no extra time. When will the game finish?

_____

d. A train leaves London at 9:50am, and is scheduled to arrive in Edinburgh at 3:32pm. If it is delayed for 34 minutes, calculate the new time of arrival.

_____

The return journey has no delays. If the train leaves Edinburgh at 5pm, when will it arrive in London?   _____

CAN YOU?

- [ ] Recognise that shapes with the same areas can have different perimeters.
- [ ] Use the correct formulae to calculate the perimeter and area of quadrilaterals.
- [ ] Calculate the area of triangles and parallelograms.
- [ ] Use the correct formula to calculate the volume of cubes and cuboids.
- [ ] Use a variety of units, including cm and m, for all calculations.

SKILLS CHECK

Perimeter is the total length around all sides of a shape.
Area is the amount of space inside a 2D shape.
Volume is the amount of space a 3D object takes up. If the object is a container, like a box or a swimming pool, we call it capacity.

Using formulae for perimeter and area (The shapes below are not drawn to scale.)

Shape	Example	Perimeter	Area
Square	2cm, 2cm, 2cm, 2cm	$P = 4s$ $P = 4 \times 2 = 8cm$	$A = s^2$ $A = 2^2 = 4cm^2$
Rectangle	5m, 3m, 3m, 5m	$P = 2w + 2h$ $P = 2 \times 3 + 2 \times 5 = 16cm$	$A = wh$ $A = 3 \times 5 = 15m^2$
Triangle	5cm, 5cm, 3cm, 8m	To calculate the perimeter, add the sides: $P = 5 + 8 + 5 = 18cm$	$A = \frac{1}{2}bh$ $A = \frac{1}{2} \times 8 \times 3 = 12cm^2$
Parallelogram	13m, 12m, 5m	To calculate the perimeter, add the sides: $P = 5 + 13 + 5 + 13 = 36m$	$A = bh$ $A = 5 \times 12 = 60m^2$

Using formulae for volume (The shapes below are not drawn to scale.)

Shape	Example	Volume
Cube	2cm	$V = s^3$ $V = 2 \times 2 \times 2 = 8cm^3$
Cuboid	7m, 4m, 2m	$V = hdw$ $V = 2 \times 4 \times 7 = 56m^3$

PRACTICE

1. Calculate these perimeters.

    a. A square tile, with each side 6cm: _____

    b. A rectangular lawn, 4m by 8m: _____

2. Calculate these areas.

    a. A square swimming pool, 10m by 10m: _____

    b. A rectangular book 12cm by 20cm: _____

3. **Calculate the areas and complete this chart.** (The shapes are not shown to scale.)

Shape	Example	Formula to use	Area
Parallelogram	2m / 6m		
Triangle	3cm / 4cm		

4. Calculate these volumes.

    a. A cuboid, 3cm wide, 4cm high, 5cm deep: _____

    b. A cube, each side 7m: _____

5. **A shed with a flat roof is put in a garden. Its shape is cuboid. It is 5m wide, 2.5m long and 3m high. Calculate:**

    a. the area of its floor: _____

    b. the floor's perimeter: _____

    c. the shed's capacity: _____

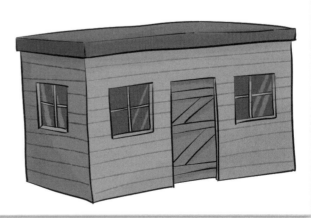

CAN YOU?

☐ Compare and sort geometric 2D shapes.

☐ Draw accurate 2D shapes using given angles and dimensions.

☐ Find unknown angles in triangles, quadrilaterals and regular polygons.

☐ Recognise and make simple 3D shapes, including nets.

SKILLS CHECK

Regular polygons

You can use what you know about shapes to identify them. Look at this diagram. Name each shape.

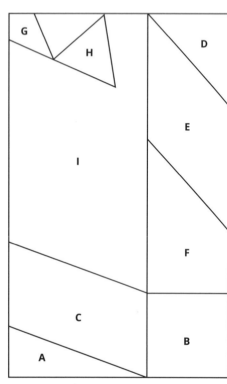

The whole shape is a rectangle (opposite sides equal; all angles 90°)

A is a right-angled scalene triangle (sides and angles are all different; one angle is 90°)

B is a square (quadrilateral; all sides equal; all angles 90°)

C is a parallelogram (quadrilateral; opposite sides equal and parallel; opposite angles equal)

D is a right-angled isosceles triangle (two sides equal; two angles equal; one angle is 90°)

E is a rhombus (quadrilateral; all sides equal; opposite angles equal)

F is a trapezium (quadrilateral; only one pair of parallel sides)

G is a kite (quadrilateral; adjacent sides equal; one pair of opposite angles equal)

H is an equilateral triangle (all sides equal; all angles 60°)

I is a hexagon (six sides)

3D shapes

Shape							
Name	cube	cuboid	cone	sphere	cylinder	triangular prism	pyramid
Faces	6	6	2	1	3	5	5
Edges	12	12	1	0	2	9	8
Vertices	8	8	0	0	0	6	5

 **PRACTICE**

1. Name these quadrilaterals.

   a. Opposite angles equal; opposite sides parallel and equal: _____

   b. All sides equal; opposite angles equal: _____

   c. Adjacent sides equal; one pair of opposite angles equal: _____

2. Draw each of these triangles. One side has been drawn for you.

a. An equilateral triangle with side length 3cm.	**b.** An isosceles triangle with two angles equal to 75°, base = 4cm.	**c.** A right-angled triangle, with a base of 3cm and one angle of 50°.

3. Draw tabs on this net that would allow someone to cut it out and stick it together.

   Name the shape: _____

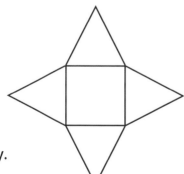

4. One of these nets is incorrect. Circle it, and then explain why.

   a.    **b.** 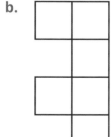   **c.**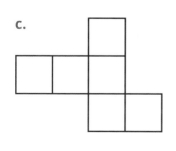

CAN YOU?

- [ ] Draw and name the different parts of a circle.
- [ ] Know that the diameter of a circle is twice the radius.
- [ ] Recognise and find angles where lines meet at a point, intersect a straight line, or are vertically opposite.
- [ ] Find missing angles.

SKILLS CHECK

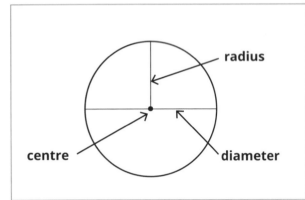

The **circumference** is the line around the circle, its **perimeter**.
The **radius** is the length from the centre to the circumference.
The **diameter** is **twice** the radius.

Make sure you can use a **protractor** properly. You should be able to measure **angles** accurately.

- Acute angles are less than 90°.
- Right-angles are 90°.
- Obtuse angles are more than 90° and less than 180°.
- Angles on a straight line add up to 180°.
- Reflex angles are more than 180° and less than 360°.
- 360° is a complete turn.

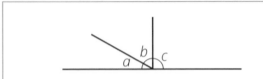

$a + b = 90°$ $a + b + c = 180°$
a and b are acute c is a right-angle

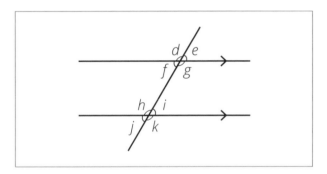

Vertically opposite angles are equal:

$d = g$ $e = f$ $h = k$ $i = j$

Corresponding angles on parallel lines are equal:

$d = h$ $e = i$ $f = j$ $g = k$

Alternate angles on parallel lines are equal:

$g = h$ $f = i$

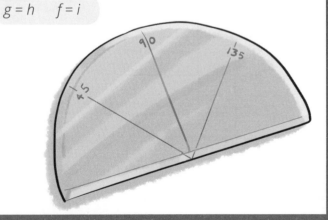

PRACTICE

1. Draw each angle.

a. 124°

b. 15°

c. 100°

d. 90°

2. Calculate the missing angles. (The diagrams are not drawn to scale.)

a.

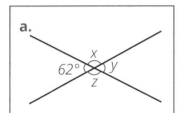

x = _____

y = _____

z = _____

b.

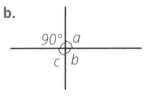

a = _____

b = _____

c = _____

c.

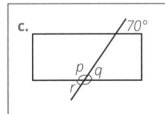

p = _____

q = _____

r = _____

d.

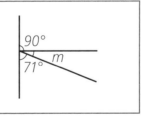

m = _____

3. Draw these circles. On each one, draw and label the radius and the diameter.

a. radius = 2cm

b. diameter = 5cm

CAN YOU?

- [ ] Identify and plot coordinates in all four quadrants on a coordinate grid.

- [ ] Draw and translate simple shapes.

- [ ] Reflect shapes in both axes.

- [ ] Recognise, describe and continue patterns involving shapes.

SKILLS CHECK

You can plot points at **coordinates**.

You always say the x-coordinate first, and then the y-coordinate.

Point A has coordinates (1, 1), B = (−4, 3), C = (2, −1), D = (−3, −4), E = (0, 3), F = (−1, 0)

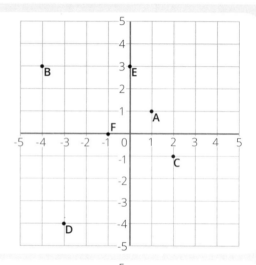

If **translating** a shape, all the vertices of the shape move the same amount in the x direction and the y direction.

The translation in this grid is 6 right and 5 up.

Remember, translations can also go left and down.

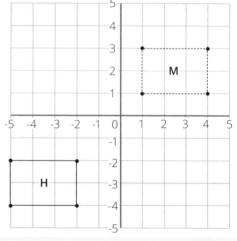

In **reflections** a vertical or horizontal line can act like a mirror.

Look at the coordinate grid. The triangle P has been reflected in the x-axis (triangle Q) and was then reflected in the y-axis (triangle R).

Look carefully to see how the coordinates of reflected points change.

vertex (5, −3) → (5, 3) → (−5, 3)
vertex (4, −5) → (4, 5) → (−4, 5)
vertex (3, −5) → (3, 5) → (−3, 5)

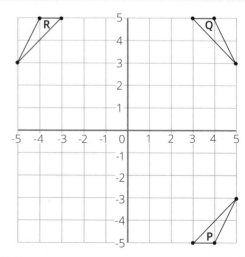

PRACTICE

1. Write down the coordinates for each point on the grid.

A (___ , ___)   B (___ , ___)   C (___ , ___)

D (___ , ___)   E (___ , ___)   F (___ , ___)

2. Plot these points on the same grid.

K (6, 1)   L (3, 0)   M (4, −2)

P (8, 8)   Q (0, −4)   R (0, 0)

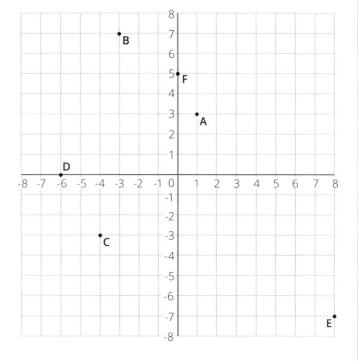

3. Translate the triangle STW 4 down and 3 left.

4. Reflect the triangle XYZ in the *x*-axis, and then in the *y*-axis.

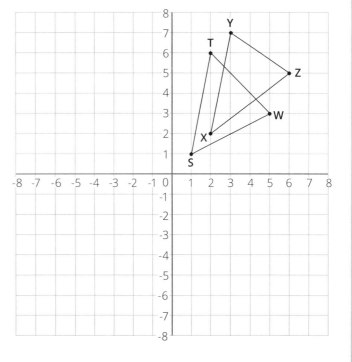

CAN YOU?

☐ Interpret and construct pie charts and line graphs to solve problems.

☐ Calculate and interpret the mean as an average.

SKILLS CHECK

Pie charts

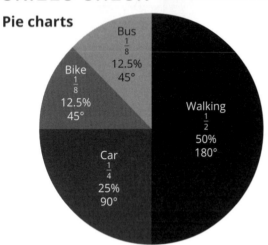

Pie charts represent proportions.

You can see from this pie chart that half the children walk to school, and that fewest take the bus or use a bike. If you know how many children there are in the school, you can calculate how many use each form of transport. For example, if there were 200 children, the pie chart would show that 100 walk, 50 come by car, 25 by bike and 25 by bus.

Line graphs

Line graphs have an x-axis and a y-axis. Points are plotted and lines drawn between them. They often show the relationship between distance and time or temperature and time. On a distance and time graph, a horizontal line means the object is standing still.

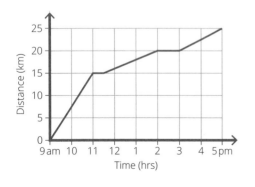

Currency conversion graphs

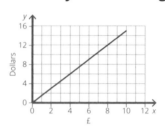

Currency conversion graphs are always a straight line that goes though the origin (0, 0).

You can see that $4 = £3, and you can use the graph to convert from dollars to pounds.

Mean

To calculate the **mean**, add all the data together, and divide by how many pieces of data there are.

This table shows the results of a traffic counting survey over 5 days. Total number of cars = 190, so the mean number of cars per day is 190 ÷ 5 = 38

Day	Mon	Tues	Wed	Thurs	Fri
Cars	37	42	57	26	28

You can also use the mean to help you find missing data. Here's a survey of bicycles where the mean is 6:

Day	Mon	Tues	Wed	Thurs	Fri
Bicycles	6		4	8	7

Tuesday is missing, but because you know the mean, you can find Tuesday's count.

total ÷ days = mean

total = mean × days

total = 6 × 5 = 30

So, total = 6 + Tuesday + 4 + 8 + 7 = 30

Tuesday + 25 = 30

So there must have been 5 bikes on Tuesday.

PRACTICE

1. Use the pie chart to answer these questions.

Pie chart of pet ownership in a class of 30 children

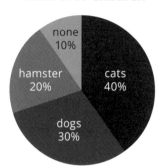

a. How many children have each type of animal?

cat _____   dog _____

hamster _____   none _____

b. What fraction of the class have each type of animal?

cat _____   dog _____

hamster _____   none _____

c. How many degrees is each sector of the pie chart?

cat _____   dog _____

hamster _____   none _____

2. Use the currency conversion graph to answer these questions.

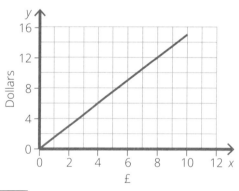

a. How many dollars is £8? _____

b. How many pounds is $8? _____

c. Estimate how many dollars are worth £1.

_____

d. How many dollars are worth £80? _____

3. Calculate the mean for each of these data sets.

a. 30, 36, 42   _____

b. 96, 97, 97, 94, 97, 90, 98, 95, 92, 94   _____

4. The mean temperature in one week in July was 22°C. What was the temperature on Friday? Complete the table.

Monday	Tuesday	Wednesday	Thursday	Friday	Saturday	Sunday
19	23	22	24		23	22

CAN YOU?

 Understand the test paper.

SKILLS CHECK

Read the questions carefully. Then read them again. Make sure you understand what the question is asking you to do.

If a question asks you to 'Show your method' then there will be marks if you get the method correct, even if your answer is wrong.

If you're struggling with a question, move on and return to it at the end.

Write as clearly as you can.

Try to spend the last five minutes checking your work. Do your answers look about right?

If you have time to spare and have a few questions unanswered, just have a go – you don't lose marks for trying.

Remember: for a long division or long multiplication, you can get a mark for showing your method, even if your answer is wrong.

Before calculating, remember to work out whether a mental or written method would be most appropriate.